A Whole Entire Book of

THINGS I LOVE ABOUT YOU

1

When we're together,
you make me want to

kiss your face forever.

2

I'm a tiny bit obsessed
with your

hair, eyes, nose, lips, butt, boobs.

3

Nobody has ever made me

feel loved and safe

the way you do.

4

I love to watch you

on facetime when we Netflix party

but not in a creepy way.

5

I suspect you might secretly
hold the world record for

being the most beautiful girl in the world.

6

I love all your body parts,
but if I had to pick a favorite,
it would be your

eyes because I can see our future in them.

7

If you were an ice cream flavor, you'd be

Mint Chocolate Chip,

because you're

fresh asf (like mint)

and

sweet like chocolate.

(and its my fav)

8

I love how passionate
you are about

Musical theater.

9

Your

body, face, everything

is truly remarkable.

Look at me, remarking on it.

10

I really admire the way you

are passionate about the things you love.

11

When I think about your

existence ______________________,

I feel

butterflies ______________________

inside.

12

I love how you
encourage me to

love & take care of myself

13

I love how you love me
even though I

may not feel I deserve it.

14

And you never make me
feel bad about my

past & mental illness
______________________________.

15

I know it's hard to believe,
but I love you even more than

I love Twilight ______________.

16

I just think your

Personality
____

is so

beautiful
_______________.

17

Okay, fine, I'll admit it:
I even love your

love for Poussey
______________________________.

18

You inspire me to be more

compastionate & understanding

19

I always want to hear
your thoughts on

everything
______________________________.

(Although I might disagree.)

20

I love how you're not afraid to use your

voice to stand up & speak out about injustices happening in the world

21

You have excellent taste in

literally everything.

22

I think of you fondly
every time I hear

1980's Horror film, Somewhere only we Know, I found a girl, She, coffee

23

I wish we could run away to

New Zeland
____

together.

24

I don't want to

experience this life

with anyone but you.

25

I even love the way you hate

the thought that Im with you
because of Bella from Twilight

(which isnt true)

26

If I could go back in time, I'd

be ______________________

with you.

Sooner.

27

I love the way you

are & look.

Even when you're

Insecure.

Youre the most
beautiful girl in the
world

28

I really love touching your

butt hehe ____________________.

(Maybe more than I should?)

29

You're the best

girlfriend
____

in the universe.

30

You make me so

Simpy
______________________________,

it's a little embarrassing.

I Love

YOU!

FILL IN THE *Love*®

Created, published, and distributed by Emily McDowell & Friends
11111 Jefferson Blvd. #5167
Culver City, CA 90231
emilymcdowell.com
Emily McDowell & Friends is a trademark of Knock Knock LLC
Fill in the Love is a registered trademark of Knock Knock LLC

Printed in China

ISBN: 9781642445626
UPC: 812729026472

10 9 8 7 6 5